The Merrill Linguistic Reading Program

Third Edition

Based on the philosophy of Charles C. Fries

Authors:
Rosemary G. Wilson
Mildred K. Rudolph

Consultants:
Heather Elko
Timothy E. Heron
Lois Michel Plous
Betsy Small
Goldie Wilson

Editorial Coordinator:
Judith Willard Kinney

Production Coordinator:
Gwendolyn Joslin Hiles

Editor:
Ruth Bradfield Cochrane

Contributing Editor:
Deborah C. Damian

Project Designer:
Richard C. Cantrell

Project Artist:
R. Ann Diehl

Charles E. Merrill Publishing Co.

TABLE OF CONTENTS

Published by
Charles E. Merrill Publishing Co.

bit   bits

fit   fits

hit   hits

sit   sits

it's

for

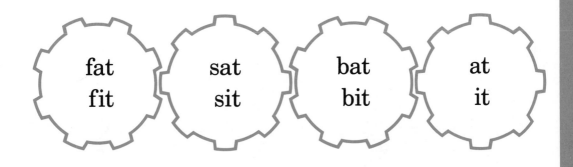

fat   sat   bat   at

fit   sit   bit   it

On Jan's Lap

Can Nat sit on Jan's lap?

Nat can sit on her lap.

Nat sat on Jan's lap.

Rags ran to see Jan.

Can she and Nat fit on Jan's lap?

She and Nat can fit.

Jan pats Rags and Nat on her lap.

Nat and Rags

Nat sits on Sam's lap.

Sam pats the cat.

Rags can see Nat on Sam's lap.

She is sad.

Can Rags fit on Sam's lap?

She can.

Rags and Nat nap.

Can It Fit?

Sam had a hat in a bag.
It's not his hat.

Is it for Dan?
Sam fits the hat on Dan.
It fits!
It is Dan's hat.

Sam and Rags

Sam and Rags sat in the van.

Sam had a ham in a bag.

It's a fat ham.

Rags bit the bag.

Is Sam mad at Rags?

He is not mad.

He had a bit for Rags.

She wags and wags.

Nat and the Map

Sam had a map in the van.

Nat looks at it.

Nat hits and hits the map.

He hit it and bit it.

Sam had to look at the map.

It's in bits!

He looks at Nat.

Bad Nat!

It's bad to hit Sam's map!

pin pins

win wins

tin

into

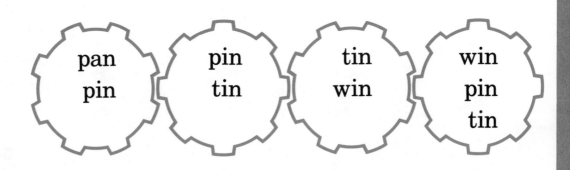

A Tin Can

Jan sees a tin can.
She hits the can into the van.

Jan looks for it in the van.
It is in the van.

Jan hits the can into a bag.

Dan's Fan

Dan had a fan.

Rags can see it.

She bit the fan.

Dan ran to Rags.

Rags!

Not the fan!

The fan is tin!

It can hit Rags.

Rags is sad.

A Pin for Jan

A man had pins for caps.

The man can see Dad.

Can Dad win a pin for Jan's cap?

Dad wins a pin.

He pins it on her cap.

Jan had a pin on her cap.

A Bag, a Cap, and a Pin

Dad had a cap for Dan.

The cap had a pin on it.

It's in a bag on his lap.

The pin can fit on Dan's cap.

The cap can fit into the bag.

The bag can fit on Dad's lap.

Jam for Dan and Jan

Dad had jam for Dan and Jan.

It's in a tin can.

Rags can see the jam.

She sits and looks at the can.

Dan and Jan look at Rags.

The jam is not for Rags.

It's for Jan and Dan.

Rags is sad.

six

fix

mix

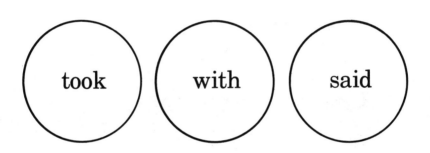

took   with   said

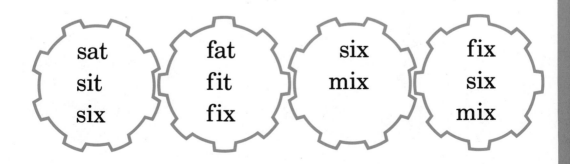

sat	fat	six	fix
sit	fit	mix	six
six	fix		mix

I Am Tam

I am Tam.

I am in the van with Dan
and Jan.

Sam had to fix the van.

I can look at his maps.

Jan and Dan can tag and bat.

Sam can fix the van.

Tags and Bags

Tam is in the van.
"I can mix the tags on the bags,"
she said.

Sam looks for his bag.
He took a bag.
The bag is not his.

Sam looks at Tam.
"It's bad to mix tags on bags,"
he said.

Tam is not sad.
She can fix the tags.

A Cap in a Bag

Dan's cap is on a mat.

Nat looks at the cap.

He bit it and hit it.

He hit it into a bag.

Dan had to look for his cap.

Tam is with Dan.

"Look in the bag, Dan," she said.

Dan said, "It's in the bag.

It's a rag!"

Pins and a Rag

Tam had a bag with six pins in it.

"I can fix Nat's mat with a rag,"

she said.

She pins a rag on the mat.

"It's a bad fit," she said.

"I can fix it with Jan's rag."

Tam pins Jan's rag on the mat.

It fits!

Jan's Maps

Jan looks for her maps.
"I had six maps in the van,"
she said.

"Tam took the six maps," said Dad.

Jan ran to Tam.
"I had six maps in Dad's van,"
said Jan.

Tam had the maps with her.
She took the maps to Jan.
Jan took the six maps to the van.

did

lid   lids

hid

rid

Sid

cannot

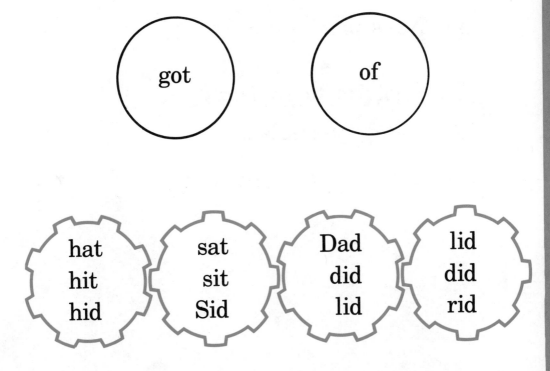

| got | of |

hat	sat	Dad	lid
hit	sit	did	did
hid	Sid	lid	rid

Lids for Pans

Sam had six pans in his van.
He had lids for the pans.
Tam took a pan with a lid for Nat.
Nat took the lid and hid it.

Sam said, "Tam, fix a lid
for Nat's pan."

Tam got tin to fit Nat's pan.
She said, "Nat is bad.
He hid the lid for his pan."

A Tin Lid

A tin lid is on Nat's pan.

It's a bad fit for the pan.

Nat hit at it.

Dad cannot nap.

Dad took the lid and hid it.

"I got rid of it," he said to Dan.

"I hid it."

Nat looks for the lid.

A Mix in a Van

I am Sid.

I can fix a van.

Sid had a mix in her van.

"I cannot fix a mix in a van,"
she said.

Sid got rid of the mix.

She took it to Jan and Dan.

"Dan and Jan can fix the mix,"
she said.

Dan and Jan did fix the mix.

Jan's Cap

Tam hid Jan's tan cap.

She hid it in a bag.

Jan looks and looks for her cap.

She looks into the bag.

"Nat is a bad cat,"

Jan said to Tam.

"He hid the tan cap."

Tam said, "He did not.

I hid it."

Sid and the Tin Lid

Sid ran her van.

The lid for Nat's pan is

in the van.

Sid said, "Is a tin can

in the van?"

She looks into the van.

"It's not a can," she said.

"It's the lid for Nat's pan.

Dad hid it in the van."

Sid got rid of it.

him

rim

Jim

Kim

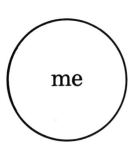

me

ham
him

jam
Jim

him
Jim
Kim

Kim
him
rim

Jim, Kim, and Jan

Sid took Jim and Kim to see Jan.

Jim, Kim, and Jan ran.

Jan said, "Look at me!

Can Kim tag me?"

Kim ran at Jan.

Kim tags her.

Jim ran and hid.

Jan and Kim had to look for him.

"Jim hid," said Jan.

"I cannot see him.

He wins!"

For Dan

Sam had a bag in his van.

A tag is on the bag.

It said, "For Dan."

In the bag is a bat for him.

Kim looks into the bag.

"Is the bat for me?" she said.

"It's for Dan," said Sam.

"I hid it in the bag."

For Jan

Dan took his bat to Jan.

"See the bat Sam got for me?"

Dan said to her.

Jan looks at Sam.

Sam had a bag with a tag.

"Is it for me?" Jan said.

The tag said, "For Jan."

In the bag is a bat for Jan.

A Bad Rim

Jim and Kim had Nat's pan.
The pan had a bad rim.
Jim took the pan to his dad.

Kim said, "Nat had a pan
with a bad rim."

Jim said, "It's bad for him.
He cannot lap at his pan."

"The rim is tin," said Dad.
"I cannot fix it."

Jim got rid of the pan.

A Tin Can and a Tin Lid

Dad had a ham in a tin can.
A lid fits on the rim of the can.

Jim and Kim look at the can.
"Is the can tin?" said Jim.

"And the lid?" said Kim.
"Is the lid tin?"

"The lid is tin," said Dad.
"And the can is tin."

lip	lips
dip	dips
tip	tips
rip	rips
zip	zips

has

as

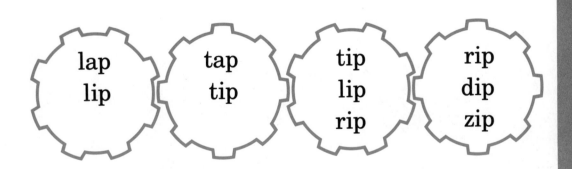

Zip the Bag

Jim cannot zip his bag.
It has a bad rip in it.
He took the bag to Kim.

Kim has pins to fix the bag.
She tips the bag to look
at the rip.
She pins it.

Jim looks at the bag
as Kim zips it.

Sid's Lip

Sid hit her lip.
She did it on the tip of a fan.

Tam has a kit.
She can fix Sid's lip.

Sid has to sit for Tam
to fix her lip.
Tam dips a pad into a can.
She pats Sid's lip with the pad.
She fits the pad on Sid's lip.

A Rip in a Bag

Jan has a ham in a bag.

Dan has to dip into the bag

for a bit of ham.

He rips the bag.

Jan looks at the bag.

She sees the rip in it.

She looks at Dan.

Dan has bits of ham on his lips.

big	
fig	figs
wig	wigs
pig	pigs
dig	digs

if

happy

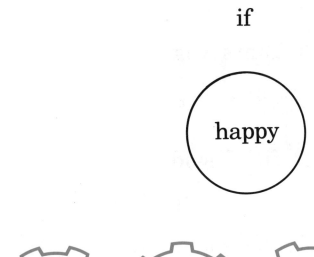

bag
big

wag
wig

big
wig
pig

pig
fig
dig

Figs and a Wig

Tam has a tan wig.

Kim has a bag of figs.

Tam took a fig and ran.

"If Tam took a fig,

I am mad," said Kim.

Kim is not a bit happy.

She took Tam's wig.

She hid it in a bag.

"Wigs for figs," said Kim.

Tam took the fig to Kim.

Kim took the wig to Tam.

Dig for Dad

Dad is not happy.

He has to dig a big pit.

He digs and digs.

Dad said, "I had to dig
a big pit, and I did."

He sat and took a nap.

Jan said, "Rags and I can dig
a big pit."

Jan and Rags dig the pit for Dad.

In the Pit

Nat digs in Dad's pit.

He hid his pan and lid in it.

Rags digs in the pit.

She hid a tin can in it.

Dad looks into his big pit.

He said, "A can, a pan, and a lid?

Did pigs dig in the pit?"

"Rags and Nat did it," said Jan,

"not a pig."

run	runs
bun	buns
fun	
sun	

your

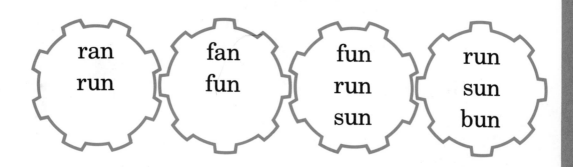

ran
run

fan
fun

fun
run
sun

run
sun
bun

Not in the Sun

"Jim, run and tag me.
It's fun," said Tam.

"Not in the sun," said Jim.
"It's not fun if I run
in the sun."

Tam runs to Kim.
"Run and tag me," she said.

"It's not fun to run in the sun,"
said Kim.

"I can run in the sun,"
said Tam.
"It's fun for me!"

Six Buns

Kim ran and got six buns
for her dad.
She took the buns to him.

"I got six big buns,"
she said to him.

"Six buns in a bag," said Dad.

"A bun for me, a bun for Dan,"
said Kim.
"A bun for Jan, a bun for Tam.
And buns for Dad and Jim."

Pins for Caps

Jim had a pin on his cap.
Kim said, "Is the pin
on your cap tin?"

"It's a tin pin," said Jim.

Jan's cap has a pin on it.
"I had to run to win it,"
said Jan.

Jan and Jim had pins.
Kim did not.
Jim said, "If Kim runs,
she can win a pin."
Is Kim happy?

Not a Bit for Rags

Tam took a bun to Jan.
The bun had bits of fig in it.
Rags looks at the bun
and wags at Tam.

Jan said, "Fix a bit of your bun
for Rags, Tam."

"A bun with figs is bad for Rags,"
said Tam.

Rags is not happy.
She is sad.

Bat a Run

Dan is not happy.

He had to bat in a run to win.

He said, "I cannot bat if I look into the sun."

His dad said, "Fix your cap."

Dan did as his dad said.

He bats in a run and wins.

but

cut   cuts

nut   nuts

hut   huts

have

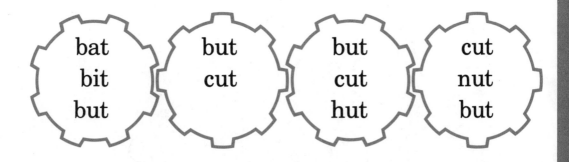

bat   but   but   cut

bit   cut   cut   nut

but   hut   but

A Big Bun

Sid had a big bun in a bag.

The bun had nuts on it.

Sid said, "I have to cut the bun

into six bits."

She rips the bag and cuts the bun.

"I have a bun with nuts,"

said Sid.

"I have bits of bun for Jim, Kim,

Dan, Jan, Tam, and me."

Dad's Van

Dad's van cannot run,
but he can fix it.
"Run and look at the pigs
in the huts," said Dad.

Dan ran to a hut.

He can run and have fun.
But Dad has to fix his van.
It's not fun for Dad.

A Cut in a Bag

Jim has a bag,

but he cannot zip it.

He took it to his dad.

His dad can fix it for him.

Jim's dad has to cut into the bag.

He cuts and cuts.

Kim said, "Look, Jim!

Look at the big cut in your bag!"

His dad said, "It's a big cut,

but I can fix it."

And fix it he did.

Not for Rags

Tam got buns for Jan and Dan.
She got big buns
with nuts and figs.
She had to cut the buns.
Rags looks at the bun
with the nuts on it.

Tam cut the bun with the nuts.
She had a bit for Jan and for Dan,
but not for Rags.
"Rags cannot have a nut," she said.
Rags is sad.

Fix a Fan

Sid has a fan,

but the fan cannot run.

It has a bad rim.

Sid looks for Dan's dad.

"I can fix a van, but I cannot

fix a fan," Sid said to him.

Dad tips the fan and looks at it.

He cuts a bit of tin.

He taps it on the bad rim.

"Your dad can fix fans,"

said Sid to Dan.

cup cups

pup pups

up

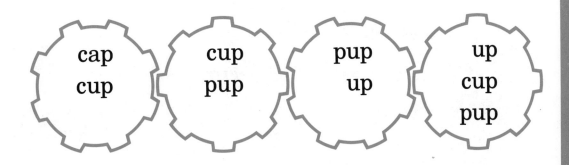

A Cut Lip

Jim cut his lip on a cup.
Tam took Jim and the cup
to her dad.
She said, "Look
at Jim's lip, Dad.
He cut it on a cup."

Dad said, "Look up at me, Jim.
I have to look at your lip.
It's bad to have a cup
if it cuts your lip."

Jim looks up as Tam's dad fits
a pad on his lip.
Tam got rid of the cup.

Tam's Pup

Tam has a tan pup.

Dan said, "Tam, look at your pup.

He has a cup, and it has

a bad rim."

The pup runs to Tam with the cup.

He sits up for Tam,

but she is not happy.

"Pups cannot have cups

with bad rims," she said.

The pup sits on Tam's lap,

and she pats him.

The Pup and the Cup

Tam got rid of the cup
with the bad rim.
But her pup digs it up.
He runs to Rags with it.
Rags and the pup run and run
with the cup.

Kim said to Tam, "Your pup has
the cup with the bad rim.
It can cut him."

Tam ran to Rags and the pup.
She took the cup and hid it.

bug	bugs
jug	jugs
hug	hugs
rug	rugs
tug	tugs

are

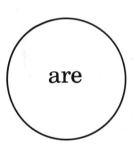

bag	rag	tag	bug
big	rug	tug	hug
bug		hug	jug

A Bug in the Van

Kim is in the van with Jan.

Jan looks up and sees a bug.

She tugs at Kim.

"Look, Kim," she said.

"It's a big bug!"

"It's not a bad bug," said Kim.

She hugs Jan, but Jan

is not happy.

"Hit it," said Jan.

Kim fans at the bug and taps it.

Jan is happy.

Kim got rid of the bug.

A Bug on a Rug

Jim and Kim are on a rug.

A bug runs on the rug.

It runs into Kim's jug.

It runs into Jim's cup.

"Hit it, Kim!" said Jim.

"Hit the bug with your cap!"

Kim taps the bug,

and Jim has a hug for Kim.

A Bad Pup

"Tam's pup is bad," said Jan
to Kim.
"He tugs at rugs.
He bats at bugs.
He tips jugs.
He digs in pits.
He is a bad pup."

"He is not bad," said Kim.
"He is a happy pup,
and happy pups dig and tug."

bus

Gus

us

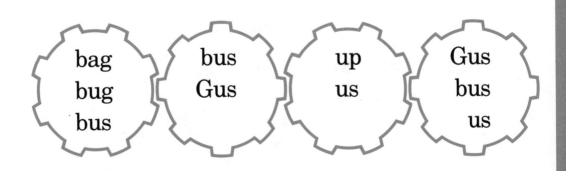

bag
bug
bus

bus
Gus

up
us

Gus
bus
us

Fun for Jim and Kim

Jim and Kim are with Jan.

Jim said to Jan, "Gus took us
on his bus.

He took us to look at the pigs.

Gus had to fix the bus,
and I sat with him.

I had maps to look at.

Kim ran to look at the pigs."

Jan said, "It's fun to look
at pigs in huts!"

"But I had fun with Gus
and the maps," said Jim.

On the Bus

Gus runs a big bus.

Jan and Tam are on the bus.

Tam has her pup on her lap.

Kim runs to sit with Jan

and Tam.

"I have a bun for us," she said.

She cuts the bun into bits.

"Have a bit of bun," she said

to Tam's pup.

The pup wags and wags.

Kim hugs the pup.

Six on a Bus

Jim and Kim are on a bus.

Jim said, "Look at us

on a big bus.

We are with Gus,

and he runs the bus.

Jan and her dad are with us.

Six of us are on the bus."

Kim said, "It's not six, is it?"

Jan said, "It is six.

Rags got on with us."

hum   hums

gum

ham   hum   gum   hum
him   gum   hum   hums
hum

Kim and Little Bud

Kim and Pam are on the bus
with Gus.
Kim sees her cat, Little Bud.
"Gus, look at Little Bud!"
she said.
She ran and got the cat.

But Little Bud is in the mud.
Kim got mud on her and mud
on the bus.
She and Gus are not a bit happy.

Little Pam

Gus is Pam's dad.
Little Pam took him to look at
the pigs in the huts.

Pam ran to look at the pigs.
Gus said, "Pam!
Look at your hat!
It's in the mud!"

Gus had to dip into the mud
for Pam's hat.
Pam is sad, but Gus said,
"A little bit of suds
can fix your hat."

Mud on the Van

Pam and Kim are with Sam
on his van.
It ran into the mud.
Pam said, "Look at the mud
on the van.
I have to have rags
and a pan of suds."

Pam got the pan of suds.
Kim got the rags.
Pam and Kim dip into the suds.

Kim, Pam, and Sam got rid
of the mud on the van.

mud

Bud

suds

little

mad
mud

bad
Bud

Sid
Sid's
suds

Bud
mud
suds

Gum for Pam

Gus has a little bag for Pam.

"Pam, look in the bag," he said.

Pam sees gum in the bag.

She hums, "A bag of gum for me.

I am happy!"

But the bag has a rip in it.

The gum is in the mud.

Pam looks for the gum,

but she did not hum.

Not Fit for a Pup

Pam had a bag with gum in it.

Her pup bit into the bag.

The gum is in the mud.

The pup ran to Kim with the gum.

Kim said to Pam, "Your pup

has gum with mud on it."

Kim tugs at the gum,

but the pup runs to Pam.

Pam took the gum.

She said, "It's not fit for me,

and it's not fit for a pup.

It has mud on it."

She hugs her pup.

Mud on a Pup

Pam's pup ran into the mud.

He ran into the mud for the gum.

"Pam! Your pup has mud on him!"

said Kim.

Pam said, "I have rags

and a pan of suds for us."

Pam hums as she dips the rags

into the suds.

"I got rid of the mud

on the pup," she hums.

Her pup wags and wags.

rub	rubs
tub	tubs
cub	cubs

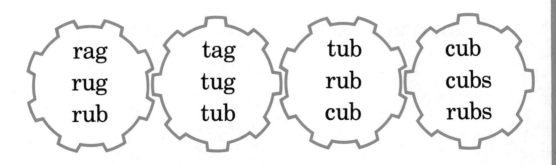

rag	tag	tub	cub
rug	tug	rub	cubs
rub	tub	cub	rubs

A Pup and a Cub

Pam's pup is in the tub,
and Pam rubs him with a rag.
Tam runs in.

"Pam cannot have cubs in tubs,"
she said to Pam.

"It's not a cub," said Pam.
"It's a pup!"

"Can I rub suds on the pup?"
said Tam.

Tam and Pam rub suds on the pup.

Suds on a Pup

Pam's pup runs up to Kim.
He has suds on him.

Kim said, "I have a tub
and a rag.
I can rub Pam's pup."
She rubs and rubs.

Kim took the pup to Pam.
"Wag for Kim," said Pam
to her pup.
"She got rid of the suds."

TO THE TEACHER

The MERRILL LINGUISTIC READING PROGRAM consists of eight Readers developed on linguistic principles applicable to the teaching of reading. The rationale of the program and detailed teaching procedures are described in the Teacher's Edition of each Reader.

All words introduced in this Reader are listed on the following pages under the headings "Words in Pattern," "Sight Words," and "Applications of Patterning."

Words listed as "Words in Pattern" represent additional matrixes in the first major set of spelling patterns. Pattern words introduced in this Reader have the matrixes -it, -in, -ix, -id, -im, -ip, -as, -ig, -un, -ut, -up, -ug, -us, -ud, -um, and -ub. The one-word pattern if is also presented. The consonant letters k, z, and g appear in initial positions for the first time. In addition, some pattern pages present combinations of words (compound words) and pattern words with the ending -s.

Words listed as "Sight Words" are high-frequency words introduced to provide normal sentence patterns in the stories.

Words listed as "Applications of Patterning" include new words based on patterns and sight words previously introduced, additional tense forms, plurals, and possessives.

WORD LISTS FOR TEACHER REFERENCE

Pages	Words in Pattern		Sight Words
Unit 1 5-10	bit	bits	for
	fit	fits	
	hit	hits	
	sit	sits	
	it's		
Unit 2 11-16	pin	pins	
	win	wins	
	tin		
	into		
Unit 3 17-22	six		took
	fix		
	mix		with
			said
Unit 4 23-28	did		got
	lid	lids	
	hid		of
	rid		
	Sid		
	cannot		
Unit 5 29-34	him		me
	rim		
	Jim		
	Kim		
Unit 6 35-38	lip	lips	
	dip	dips	
	tip	tips	
	rip	rips	
	zip	zips	
	has		
	as		

Pages	Words in Pattern		Sight Words
Unit 7 39-42	big		happy
	fig	figs	
	wig	wigs	
	pig	pigs	
	dig	digs	
	if		
Unit 8 43-48	run	runs	your
	bun	buns	
	fun		
	sun		
Unit 9 49-54	but		have
	cut	cuts	
	nut	nuts	
	hut	huts	
Unit 10 55-58	cup	cups	
	pup	pups	
	up		
Unit 11 59-62	bug	bugs	are
	jug	jugs	
	hug	hugs	
	rug	rugs	
	tug	tugs	
Unit 12 63-66	bus		
	Gus		
	us		
Unit 13 67-70	mud		little
	Bud		
	suds		
Unit 14 71-74	hum	hums	
	gum		
Unit 15 75-77	rub	rubs	
	tub	tubs	
	cub	cubs	

Applications of Patterning
(The underlined numbers are page numbers.)

Unit 1	Unit 4	Unit 7	Unit 10	Unit 13
5-10	23-28	39-42	55-58	67-70
looks	pans	pit	rims	Pam
	tan	Tam's		Pam's

Unit 2	Unit 5	Unit 8	Unit 11	Unit 14
11-16	29-34	43-48	59-62	71-74
caps	. . . .	. . . .	Kim's	. . . .
sees			pits	

Unit 3	Unit 6	Unit 9	Unit 12	Unit 15
17-22	35-38	49-54	63-66	75-77
tags	kit	fans	we	. . . .
Tam	pad	Jim's		
	Sid's			